"If the current rate of destruction continues unabated, there will be little rainforest left on our planet by the year 3000. How extraordinarily ironic that, as we enter the biotech millennium and Mother Nature becomes ever more promising as a source of new raw materials for medicines, we are destroying ecosystems at an ever increasing rate. Hopefully, it is not too late to take a moment to pause and reflect on the toll our society takes on the health of our planet and decide how we can make a mid-course correction.

This book opens a pathway for thinking about our future."

—**Mark Plotkin, Ph.D.**
PRESIDENT, AMAZON CONSERVATION TEAM

"...provided the most thoughtful, stimulating and fun discussions we have ever had with our children."

—**Paul Jünger Witt**
PRODUCER OF THE FILM THREE KINGS

" Technological advances have launched a new age of communication. At this time humans have a unique opportunity to step back and envision how these advances can dramatically improve our quality of life. This book creatively stimulates that important thinking process."

—**Maggie Wilderotter**
CEO, WINK COMMUNICATIONS

" 'Progress' has put the very survival of our living planet in jeopardy. Imagining what could be, for better or worse, will help us choose the future we want. This book, in a fun easy way, help us envision and decide."

—**Fred Krupp**
EXECUTIVE DIRECTOR OF EDF

Dear Beth + Eric —

Wishing you two a

wonderful and fulfilling

New Millennium together!

BRAINTICKLERS™

Beyond Y2K—Questions for the New Millennium and the Year 3000

ELIZABETH ARNOLD AND ROD BECKSTRÖM

© Copyright 1999 by Elizabeth Arnold and Rod Beckström

All rights reserved. Published 1999

Printed in the United States of America

ISBN 0-9675731-0-6

No part of this book may be reproduced in any form or by any electronic or
mechanical means including information storage and retrieval systems without
permission in writing from the publisher, except by a reviewer, who may
quote brief passages in a review.

Published by:
Brainticklers™ Publishing
1592 Union St., Suite 325
San Francisco, CA 94123
Phone: (415) 441-2418
Fax: (415) 441-3248
Web: www.brainticklers.com

The Library of Congress Cataloging-in-Publication Data
available upon request

Arnold, Elizabeth
Beckström, Rod

ISBN 0-9675731-0-6

Acknowledgments

We thank everyone who has contributed to our lives. In addition, we would like to thank some people who have contributed to this book. We took to heart Scott Cook's positive feedback on the questions and suggestions for publishing and electronic distribution. Our thanks go to Kathy Hawk for her editorial polishing and for some great questions. Bert Lund and other friends also contributed insightful ideas. Kim Carlisle provided excellent, timely and professional assistance in copy editing. Christine Arthur dressed up our questions in an elegant design and masterfully turned our project around on a dime. Our thanks also go to Webmama, Barbara Coll, Diana Trott for her marketing and publicity expertise and Jill Ziegler for her professional graphic services. Last but first, we thank God for giving us the opportunity to experience the present as it slides into the future.

Elizabeth Arnold and Rod Beckström

Table of Contents

Introduction

The Power of Asking Questions

Questions, especially those that tickle our brains, have the magnificent power to transform our destiny. The quality of your life is equal to the quality of the questions you ask. For example:

> "What am I doing right now that's life affirming?"
> "How can I add a little fun to my life in this moment?"
> "What can I do to make my life more exciting?"

Just by thinking about these braintickling questions, we have already changed the shape of our future.

The same holds true on a global scale. The quality of the questions asked by society equals the quality of life for our global community. If we think about the future through the form of questions, together we can raise our consciousness, make clearer choices, and change the world.

The main purpose of this book is to spark your imagination about the future—to voice how you want it to be and how you think it will unfold. Brainticklers is also about having fun! At the end of this section we will explain how to use this book for parties, events and group discussions as well as for moments of personal reflection.

Just imagine the impact on society when millions of people think and talk about braintickling questions such as:

"In the year 3000, what will keep people from catching the common cold?"

"What level of control will we have over the weather in 3000? What will be the moral and social implications of weather management?"

"What characteristics will our leaders possess in the year 3000?"

"What will life be like on Earth 1000 years from now?"

Logic and science support the power of questions. Questions jump start thoughts. Within the world of chemistry and physics, thoughts can be understood as chemical reactions with electromagnetic effects in the mind and body. Since every action ripples subtly through the universe, it appears that all thinking has universal impact. Our thoughts also shape our beliefs which, in turn, frame our every action, whether as individuals or as nations. As technology propels us forward into the age of information, thoughts have become more transformative than in any previous millennium.

Often a question must be asked before significant new thoughts occur. We ask questions about something to understand it better. The question may be answered quickly, or it may linger for decades until the answer magically pops into someone's head. Although some people believe in divine inspiration and others believe humans tap into a broader human consciousness, most of us know from personal experience that eventually our questions are answered, and the future we envision often materializes.

Here is an example from co-author Rod Beckström:

When I was growing up in Tulsa, Oklahoma, I dreamed of conducting international business on a global scale. I had never been overseas, and I had no idea of how I could put my life on a path to make that happen. Several years later I heard a teacher at my high school mention that they were initiating a foreign exchange program. I went home and announced to my parents that I was going to Germany for a year as an exchange student. That year of living in and traveling through Europe led to the opportunity to work in London and later to participate in building a global company with offices in North America, Europe, Asia, and Australia and customers in thirty countries worldwide.

Co-author Elizabeth Arnold had a similar experience:

In second grade I asked when I could go to college. In fourth grade I wrote Harvard Law School and asked how best to prepare for admission. I did not know any attorneys or Harvard graduates. Although the school sent only a form application packet in response, doors kept opening as I grew, and fifteen years later I had my Harvard Law School degree in hand.

4

Questions have changed the future on the global level as well:

In the early 1500s, Leonardo daVinci, Italian painter, sculptor, architect, engineer and scientist, studied how birds flew and created the first flying machine. He also envisioned and drew preliminary sketches for a helicopter.

Four hundred years later, brothers Orville and Wilbur Wright, American aviation pioneers and inventors of the first airplane, knew humans would travel to the moon and wondered what technology might look like to get them there. The public thought them mad.

Sixty years later, Apollo 11 landed on the moon. As he stepped onto the moon's surface, Neil Armstrong spoke words which continue to inspire us today: "That's one small step for man. One giant leap for mankind."

Coincidental? We think not. Perhaps the advances in aviation started with Leonardo. More likely, cave dwellers started thinking about human flight as they watched birds flying overhead.

Every thought we think affects how we live individually and as a member of society. The Buddhists and Hindus call it karma. Western philosophers call it the law of cause and effect. Scientists might call it kinetic electromagnetic energy. Have you ever heard the old saying, "What goes around, comes around?" It's the same idea.

This means that if each of us thinks creatively and positively about the future, we can actually help shape it just by our thoughts. We might find that every one of us has not only the power to shape our own lives, but also the power to shape the world through the questions we ask ourselves.

Why Y3K?

So why ask questions about how life could be in 3000 instead of looking just 10 years out? Because big insights usually come to us when we ask big questions. In the grand scheme of creation, 1,000 years is a trifle. Some scientists believe our universe started 12 billion years ago. On that scale, one thousand years represents only one millionth of one eighth of one percent of that time.

Or take Einstein's view that time is relative — it doesn't exist in an absolute sense. So why not stretch our sense of time out a bit further into the future and get our creative juices going?

Paul Saffo of the Institute for the Future advises us that it's fair to look 1,000 years out into the future if you also take a moment to look 1,000 years back. Let's start there.

Probably thousands of press stories have focused on many people's fears that the year 2000 will bring the end of the world. No doubt our forebears in 999 had similar concerns. In fact, when midnight mass was celebrated in the Vatican on December 31, 999, many people trembled in fear that the apocalypse would scorch the earth at midnight. They were relieved when it didn't.

In 1000, Viking longships raided budding cultures from the Russian Volga to American Vinland to the markets of the Middle East. Islamic cultures preserved precious knowledge of antiquity and extended their cosmopolitan influence across the Middle East, Asia Minor, North Africa, Spain, and Eastern Europe, but conflicts within the faith and with other cultures loomed on the horizon. The Song Dynasty in China ruled a vast empire from Kaifeng, an open city of canals, trade, and pleasure grounds, but trouble was brewing at top levels of the government. In the Americas, the great city of Teotihuacan had been abandoned and warring tribes began to jostle for supremacy. Starvation, illiteracy, war, limited transportation, disease, and slavery were part of everyday life all over the world. The global population was approximately 300 million people. Life expectancy hovered in the low thirties. Many people probably thought things couldn't get much worse.

Yet the new millennium brought unimaginable advances in technology, transportation, health care, agriculture, and human rights. Today these and many other changes continue to develop faster and faster. Advances in scientific and technological pursuits such as genetics and neurobiology, globalization of cultures by satellite communications and the Internet, and the development of "emerging" countries promise to bring startling changes.

Okay, so with all this newfangled technology and wheels of change rolling rapidly through our living and working environments, how can we imagine life in the year 3000? Even people born in this century would have had difficulty envisioning where we'd be in 1999.

Although technology rips forward at an accelerating velocity, look at what hasn't changed. We feel joy, fear, sadness, and anger the same way. We still wage war for essentially the same reasons, live with huge economic and educational disparities, fight diseases, look for love, and struggle with how best to share our resources and spend our time. The largest world religions remain essentially the same.

Getting Started

So, gentlepersons, start your engines.

You already know how to forecast the future. You plan for it everyday. If we are working, we plan for retirement. If we have children, we know they will grow out of their clothes. If we are managing businesses or households, we know many of the big decisions we will face this year or next. Even if we do not know precisely when we will need to stop for gas, we have a pretty good idea of where the road goes.

We invite you to put on your thinking caps and let your mind run free with the questions on the following pages. Begin now to create your future by thinking about how the future will unfold. Ask yourself these questions knowing that just thinking about them and discussing them with others will help shape our global future and enhance the lives of our children, grandchildren and great-grandchildren.

Brainticklers asks you to come out and play.

Rules of the Road

So, where do we start and what are the rules?

1. Use these questions solo or at parties, meetings, or dinner. One friend of ours threw a dinner party with three questions as the theme. During each course they talked about a question. Another idea is to start a meeting with a question as an icebreaker. But you are a human being, which means you are wonderfully creative. We know you'll find even more ways to play with these questions.

2. Please be sensitive to the other players. Pretend you are talking to your Aunt Cecilia. Show everyone respect. Every idea is valuable, and the goal is to get as many ideas out as possible and to enjoy the process.

3. Laugh with, but not at, others. Only dim lights laugh at true brilliance.

4. Think about how your ideas relate back to your life today. How do the choices you make today impact what the future may bring?

5. If you want to brainstorm together with others on some of the questions, please visit our website at **www.brainticklers.com**. You can add your ideas and answers to some of the questions listed, or even add your own questions! Or you can send messages to others who enjoy braintickling and make plans to link up in a chat room.

6. If we missed anything, and we may have, please let us know! We'd love to hear your ideas and share some of ours, too. You may contact us via email at **ourworld@brainticklers.com** or at the following address:

> **Brainticklers**
> 1592 Union St. #325
> San Francisco, CA 94123

Enjoy!

Elizabeth and Rod

I. Our Bodies, Our Cells

1. Who on the planet will first clone humans? Why?

2. How long will we live in 3000?
   Will people be able to live as long as
   they can afford to live?

3. If people can choose to stay at a given age or stage of physical development for as long as they would like to, what age will people select? Will women choose a different average age than men? Why?

4. When will we find the cure to AIDS?
To cancer?

5. Will the most common diseases be caused by biological elements, such as bacteria or viruses, or by non-biological causes, such as pollutants or radiation? What defensive measure will we take to avoid plagues?

6. Will medical organ farms and markets exist? Will organ warehouses contain cloned parts? How will donors be selected for cloned hands or feet, reproductive organs, brain tissue? If DNA can be mapped at birth, will donors be given a choice?

7. How will society react when technology is developed that will allow employers or insurance companies to analyze drugs, medications, and potential for disease by reading urine in workplace restrooms?

8. If we are able to identify the genes associated with all major diseases and are able to replace those with disease resistant genes, will we do so? What about replacing genes that control aging so that we could prolong life? Will we splice in gene fragments from animals in order to fight off diseases or to improve human bodies?

9. How will people choose their weight in 3000 — through genetics, food, chemicals, or by regulating diet and exercise?

10. If medical professionals can help parents choose a child's characteristics such as size, coloring, strength, etc., will the child later be able to sue for choices which the child feels have inflicted emotional pain and suffering?

11. If scientific advances can help people live for centuries, will a choice to live a natural life span be viewed as suicide or spiritual enlightenment? Will our attitudes toward dying change?

12. Will genetic re-engineering replace cosmetic surgery?

13. If everyone can look like a sitcom
    star, will "normal" and "quirky"
    become the most exotic
    characteristics of all?

14. Will people achieve greater
    happiness if they live longer?

15. What will the world population be in 3000? Will it peak before or after that date?

16. How long will human starvation continue in the new millennium? Why?

17. Will bioengineering increase or decrease the diversity of plants and animals, including humans?

18. How will we determine who has access to what medical technology? At what price?

19. Will people clone an extra set of their own organs just in case they need them? Will we insert electronic memory or thinking devices into our bodies?

20. Will a time occur when no sexually
transmitted disease can kill or maim
humans?

21. Will we learn better ways to manage our emotions naturally, or will we continue to use artificial means, such as drugs or possibly computer-based tools, to create the emotional states we desire?

22. Will new spiritual beliefs or disciplines emerge to help individuals cope with medical and technological changes in their lives?

23. In 3000, will 20th century surgery
seem as barbaric as bloodletting
does to us now? What might take
its place?

24. Will new medical approaches
    address the relationship between
    emotions, the human soul, and
    cellular biology?

25. Will we still get colds?

26. What is the highest, grandest hope
you have for human health in 3000?

II. Our Planet

27. What environmental events will trigger people to make significant changes in their consumption habits and lifestyles?

28. What percentage of today's species
of plants and animals will still be alive
in 3000?

29. If global warming begins to melt the ice caps and sea levels rise, what will happen to coastal cities and low-lying areas?

30. If the ozone layer is destroyed, how will life
    on earth react to massive doses of ultraviolet
    light? Will there be widespread blindness
    and skin cancer? What will happen to wildlife
    and plants? How will humankind cope with
    this problem?

31. Will there be changes in our beliefs about the rights of other species to exist? Will other species have a political voice?

32. When might the first environmental consumption tax be passed? Which pollutants would it tax?

33. Where will wilderness and wildlife be located in 3000? What will be the relationship between wilderness and development on the earth? What percentage of the earth's surface will be maintained as wilderness? On land? In the oceans?

34. Will we eat fish in 3000? Will it come from commercial or recreational fishing as we know it today, or will only farmed fish be left?

35. Who will oversee the future of the planet as a place that can sustain life? Will the interests of future genera-tions be represented politically?

36. What level of control will we have over the weather in 3000? Partial? Total? What will be the moral and social implications of weather management?

37. Will food grown in embryonic solutions be "purer" than food today? Will synthetic foods become more common due to changing soil conditions and declining natural genetic diversity and stocks of foodstuffs?

38. Will we be able to manage continental drift and reduce the impact of earthquakes and volcanoes?

39. How will we dispose of our waste in 3000?

40. At what year between now and 3000 will our environment be least polluted? Most polluted? What circumstances will cause these high and low points?

41. In 3000, will we be able to fully compre-
hend the language of whales or dolphins?
Of any animals? If so, what insight will help
break the translation code? Will we be
able to communicate with them through
computer-driven translators?

42. How much time will pass until we
    understand why male fertility is
    declining? What cause will be
    found?

43. What is the most positive picture of the environment you can imagine in 3000? How can you contribute to making it happen?

III. Money & Power

44. What characteristics will leaders possess in 3000? How will they differ from today's leaders?

45. How will fundamental human rights be defined in 3000? Will more or less people enjoy these rights?

46. How will democracy be defined
in 3000? Will it continue to be
associated primarily with capitalism
and free markets?

47. What new social and political movements
will be strong in 3000? How will they
value the individual versus the community,
the present versus the future, the human
species versus the earth as a whole?
What will have caused these movements
to begin and what will they accomplish?

48. How will financial markets be structured? How will money flow between individuals, businesses and governments? In 3000, what will we use for money?

49. What will we trade in 3000 that we
do not trade today? What will no
longer be traded?

50. In 3000, how will the legal code be different? Will antisocial behavior be defined as actions that hurt individuals or the community? Will punishments increase or decrease in severity?

51. How will we "prove" things if records, such as photos, tapes, etc., can be altered or created so that it is impossible to tell the difference between artificial and real evidence?

52. Will there be changes in social
tensions based on ethnic background,
gender, wealth and class? If people
remember the O.J. Simpson trial,
what will they think of it?

53. How will power, wealth and quality of life be distributed around the globe? In 3000, will there be "have" and "have-not" nations?

54. Will big cities continue to be the centers of high culture and high finance?

55. Will there be a global government in 3000? In what form?

56. In 3000, will there be a shared global
language? What will be its origin?

57. How will community planners define the ideal community? How will common and private space, individual and community concerns be balanced? Where will this type of community first be developed?

58. When people in 3000 look back at the 20th century, what leaders and events will they see as the most influential in shaping the new millennium? What will they choose to remember about the 20th century?

59. What will be taxed in 3000?
    By whom?

60. Will humans still be alive on Earth in the year 3000? If not, why not? Because of religious/spiritual events, nuclear holocaust, environmental destruction, a move to another planet, asteroid collision, or something else?

61. If you could personally define the
ideal community structure or
government in 3000, what would
it look like?

IV. Technology

62. In 3000, will the Amish be viewed
    as technological Luddites or as
    spiritual pioneers?

63. How will manufacturing change?
Will technology enable us to develop
products and manufacturing processes
that specify product elements down to
the atomic level? Inanimate as well as
animate objects?

☆ TECHNOLOGY ☆

64. Will silicon and other metallic computer components be replaced by organic thinking components? How will this affect computer processing power? Will we treat organic computers like animals or pets? Will computer diapers be a growth industry of the future?

65. When will replacement eyes be available for humans? Will these eyes simply replace normal vision or offer new spectrums of visual perception?

66. When we can match or exceed many or all human physical and mental skills with computers or appliances, how will we define our reason for being? What will be considered meaningful occupation for humans? Will smarter machines lead us to greater appreciation and cultivation of our souls?

67. Will we be able to make Brussels sprouts taste like chocolate? If complete nutrition can be packaged in any combination of taste, smell and texture, what will we choose to eat?

68. How will technology be used to maintain personal and community security? How will community security be balanced against the right to personal privacy?

69. How will we obtain news? If access to information has continued to advance, will journalists continue to exist? If so, what will be their role? If not, how will we keep abreast of events that concern us?

70. How much information will anyone know or easily learn about other people in 3000? If there are few boundaries to "information intrusion," how will we define privacy, respect for others, and honorable behavior? Will there be different standards for individuals, businesses and government?

71. What will be our primary form of communication over distances? Will new communication technologies affect our social and business values, processes or standards? Will all humans have microscopic global telephones planted in their bodies?

72. Will technology and spirituality offer the option of telepathic communication? Who will be the first to implement direct brain-to-brain or brain-to-computer communications? What will they learn?

73. How will technology affect basic human hunting and gathering?

74. How will technology affect nurturing
activities such as parenting, teaching,
counseling and nursing?

75. What will we know in 3000 about the cost of dependence on technology that we do not understand today? Will some locales or groups choose to be more technologically primitive than others? Why?

76. Will we achieve 100% literacy?
How will it happen? Or will
technology make reading and
writing obsolete disciplines by
3000?

77. In 3000, who will be able to access global communications and information systems? Will there still be a gap
    • between the technology "haves" and "have-nots?" What will the "haves" have that the "have-nots" don't?

78. As people in 3000 look back over the history of the third millennium, what will they judge to be technology's most important accomplishments and most trivial wastes of time and energy? If they could guide the technology investments of today, what would they encourage?

V. Energy & Travel

79. How will people travel in 3000? What speeds and distances of travel will they consider commonplace? How many seconds or minutes will it take to travel from New York to Tokyo?

80. How much energy will be required
    to fuel the transport of 3000?
    What will be the source of that
    energy?

81. Will the travel paths or roads in 3000 use different space than we use today? How will traffic be managed in the third millennium? Will we still drive or will we generally be driven by intelligent, traffic-flow-optimizing, safe, automated guidance systems?

82. In 3000, will people travel with personal
vehicles that move both vertically and
horizontally? Will these vehicles look more
like bicycles or diving bells? Will they
conserve fuel by incorporating human
energy?

83. Will humans live on off-world colonies on the moon or other planets? Where will these colonies be? What will be their purpose?

84. Will we have discovered sentient life
    elsewhere in the universe by 3000?
    Will we be in contact? How will
    we get along?

85. If we have extraterrestrial travel or visitors, will we quarantine arrivals to control the threat of "space pollution?" Will quarantines become an explosive issue in scientific or diplomatic communities?

86. In 3000, will we travel less or more than we do today? Will we travel for different reasons? Could technology eliminate most reasons to travel?

87. What is the best possible world of
travel that you can imagine in 3000?

VI. Inner Life

88. What new faiths, if any, will emerge by 3000?

89. To what extent will the world's faiths unify?

90. By 3000, could an advanced understanding of the role of energy in physical science, medicine, and the newer disciplines of organic technology bridge the gap between science and religion?

91. In 3000, will Einstein's theory of relativity be considered a cornerstone of scientific thought, a quack theory, or the basis of third millennium scientific exploration?

92. Will scientists prove that thought
or love travels faster than light?

93. In 3000, will most people have personal
experience of dimensions other than
we experience today? If so, how will
they describe those dimensions?
Will perceptions of new dimensions have
impact on the everyday lives of people?

94. Will we understand or experience time differently in 3000? Will our ability to plan or forecast the future be different?

95. In 3000, will we still debate the
fundamental goodness of human
nature? The existence of evil?

96. How will our understanding of the universe have changed? What will we think or feel when we look into the sky?

97. Will technological innovations, scientific discoveries, or personal development offer us access to new realms of feeling, worlds of new life forms, or mental travel to different times?

98. In 3000, what will we have discovered
about black holes in the universe?
Will we find they are doorways to worlds
that will only permit us access once we
as a species progress enough to figure
out the secret entrance codes?

99. At the close of the new millennium, what will scientists and philosophers know about the relationship of the physical universe to spiritual or metaphysical principals? Will they think differently about gravity fields, angels, entropy and chaos than we do today?

100. Will the science of physical phenomena be more detailed and complex, or reduced to a few simple principles?

101. Will we have discovered a means
to map individual human energy
profiles? Will we use these profiles
for medicine, enhanced communication or other purposes?

102. By 3000, will a universally recognized
messiah or prophet have come?
What will convince the world?
What will be the message delivered?
What will be the story of his or her life?

103. If God could advise us on the path
to building the best possible society
in 3000, what would God say?

104. How long will humans continue to discriminate against and, in some cases, kill each other in the name of God?

105. In 3000, will different nationalities, classes or social groups disagree about moral and ethical standards? Will the most universal standards be based on individual interests, family interests, community interests, planetary interests, or some other basis?

106. How will people express their spirituality in 3000? Will it be a purely personal matter, a highly public display, or something in between?

107. How will we define the soul in 3000?

108. In 3000, will the thinking that shapes government, science and the business world be based on the type of rationalism and logical analysis that currently dominates Western thinking? Will Western and Eastern philosophy draw closer together, or will human philosophy pursue a different course altogether?

109. What is the grandest vision of
     human spirit and intellect that you
     can imagine for 3000? How can an
     individual today help us arrive at
     that vision?

VII. Economy & Business

110. From mead to coffee (though wine has aged well), business beverages have gone from merry to performance fuel. What will we drink at business meetings in 3000?

111. What will the growth rate of the world economy be over the next 1000 years? Will the world economy ever stop growing?

112. If real personal income grows at 2% per annum for the next 1000 years, people will be 398 million times wealthier. Will this happen or will there be some limit to growth? How will society handle long-term zero growth if it happens?

113. How many companies today will still exist in 3000?

114. If people in the future could choose to be
ten times wealthier than they are today, and
have good health, balanced lives and a clean
environment, or twenty times wealthier
with less health, hectic lives and a destroyed
environment, which would they choose?

115. Will the U.S., Mexico and Canada unite
their currencies? Will Latin America
join? Will a global currency come into
being in the new millennium? Why will
this occur or not occur?

116. What will be the role of trade unions in 3000?

117. How much education will be
required to obtain an entry-level
job in 3000? What studies will be
required before entering work life?

118. What will be the definition of
wealth in 3000? What will be the
purpose of wealth? How will
wealth be used or stored?

119. If humans become wealthy enough to provide for their needs by working half as much time, what will the central organizational focus of society be — building community, fostering education, serving others, pursuing happiness?

120. What will it mean to be poor in 3000?

121. How will land and water rights be assigned in 3000? Fishing rights?

122. What will be the most valuable
planetary resource in 3000?
How will it be owned or traded?

123. What will be the relationship of
     wealth to political influence in 3000?
     If not wealth, what will be the chief
     precursor to individual or group
     influence?

124. Will human physical labor be a
survival requirement, an option,
or a privilege in 3000?

125. In 3000, will economic and managerial hierarchies exist as we know them? If not, what will replace them, and how will that affect efficiencies of organizations and financial markets?

126. Within what time frames will businesses plan their activities and measure their results in 3000? Milliseconds? Centuries? To whom will they report their success or failure?

127. How will business schools in 3000 use the 20th century as a teaching tool? Or will they consider the 20th century to be so primitive that it's not worth remembering or studying?

128. What is the most positive economic
     future that you can imagine for the
     earth in 3000? How much of this
     vision is possible today?

VIII. Weapons

129. When will the most destructive war occur in the new millennium? What economic or political factors will trigger it? How might it be avoided?

130. How will military weapons have changed in 3000? Will genetic engineering be used for military purposes anywhere?

131. At the end of the 20th century, people
     are allowed to kill healthy people slowly
     (by polluting or selling dangerous products
     like cigarettes), but people are not allowed
     to help unhealthy people kill themselves
     quickly (euthanasia, assisted suicide). How
     might this evolve over the next 1000 years?

132. In the 20th century, nuclear weapons were used twice — at the end of World War II. Will nuclear weapons be used again? When and by whom?

133. Will terrorism increase or decrease over the next 1000 years? How will people in 3000 deal with dissident political groups to minimize terrorism?

134. How many people will die in wars or ethnic exterminations in the next 1000 years? How can we better maintain peace in the next 1000 years?

IX. Education

135. What will the ratio of military to education expenditures be in 3000?

136. What will be the favorite fairy tales
and children's stories in 3000?

137. What will be the focus of childhood
education in 3000? How will the
subjects of study have changed?

138. How will the progress of virtual reality and
other reality-simulation technologies affect
the way education is conducted? Will
children learn more quickly? Will schools,
as we know them, exist? How will the
souls of children be affected by the changes
in media?

139. In 3000, how will young people learn community values and social skills?

140. What impact will advancing knowledge of brain function and chemistry have on theories of education?

141. How many years will be required
for a basic education in 3000?
At what age will people begin to
contribute work to the community?

142. How will competitive school sports and studies in competition, such as business education, be affected by new social philosophies or advances in scientific theory? How will people define "winning?"

143. If games are entertaining ways to practice mental and physical skills, what games will parents encourage their children to play in 3000? What games will children want to play?

144. What will children in 3000 want to be when they grow up? Who will be their heroes?

145. What will parents and educators in 3000 consider to be the optimum mix of social, emotional, scientific, verbal, technical, business and political education? How will their educational requirements be different from ours today?

X. Family Life

146. What will the nature of sexual relations be in 3000? Will sexual practices be more varied or limited when compared with today's standards?

147. How will family be defined in 3000?
Who will be included? Will we
create new social contracts to
define relationships among adults
and their offspring?

148. In 3000, how will children be born? Who will have children?

149. Who will take care of infants and toddlers in 3000? What will be considered the most important factor in baby care?

150. What will be viewed as healthy
discipline? How will it be administered?

151. What will the most popular wedding/
partnering shower present be?
Baby shower gift?

152. Will parents choose the gender and sexual preference of their children? If yes, what will be the ratio of girls to boys in different countries around the world?

153. How long will the average work week be in 3000? How will people balance their work and family life?

154. What rights will children have in 3000? At what age might children be allowed to divorce themselves from their parents?

155. What will be the nature of marriage if human life-span becomes lengthened to 200 or 1000 years? How long will the average marriage last? How many times will people marry? What kind of new marriage contracts will be created?

156. How will new self-understanding and social attitudes affect our interest in monogamy? In what form of relationships will we find the most powerful and rewarding spiritual, emotional, and sexual connections?

157. Will new in-depth knowledge of other species, such as dolphins or chimpanzees, teach us new social and family skills?

158. If satellite-networked telephone, televideo and other technologies become available and affordable to every human on the planet, what will be the impact of a hypernetworked world on family? On friendships?

☆ FAMILY LIFE ☆

159. How will families react to genetic mappings that tell them their ancestors were different people than they thought?

160. How will ethics and family values change in light of what may be profound and accelerating changes in science, technology and medicine?

161. How will family life be better in 3000 than it is now? Which of those improvements could we create today?

XI. Other Daily Life

162. What will kids want on birthdays and holidays?

163. Will we still bathe in water or have dry washes?

164. What issues will be considered too racy for dinner conversation?

165. What will one's most valued posses-
sions be? Will they be material
things or intangible traits or values?

166. Will planet and moon-bagging become the next Everest-like deeds of derring do?

167. Will people insure themselves
against genetic code theft and
replication? Will people steal hair
of great people to license illicitly
their DNA?

168. How big will homes be? What will people use to decorate and personalize their living spaces?

169. How and when will we clean our teeth? Will we have frequency toothbrushes that don't touch our teeth or dessert mouthwashes?

170. What will people in 3000 use for paper?

171. What will be the most popular pets in 3000? Will cats and dogs be genetically mixed to produce a pet with the benefits of both (a dat or a cog)?

172. Will men still wear neckties?

173. What will be the role of fashion in 3000? How many different outfits will people want? Will outfits be intelligent and dynamic, changing their structure or colors to adapt to different environments?

174. In 3000, will height and weight matter to social acceptance?

XII. Arts, Entertainment & Sports

175. Will sports still be one of the most popular pastimes in 3000? What new sports will be invented?

176. Will technology be incorporated into the contact sport games of 3000, say, for example, a 3-D playing field with limits on antigravity equipment that can be used? Will that sport require a ball, cube, or polyhedron?

177. How violent will sports be in 3000?

178. Will our dancing be communal,
individual or touching?

179. How will erotic entertainment change in the next 1000 years? Will censorship exist?

180. Will a "mass culture" exist with common entertainment content? What might replace mass culture?

181. What will be considered modern
art in 3000? What media will be
used in it? How will people in 3000
characterize our "modern art" of
today?

182. Which 20th century painters, authors and composers will be held in highest esteem? Will Jackson Pollack be appreciated more or less?

183. What new instruments will dominate percussion? Replace woodwinds?

184. Will new forms of "mood music" help people work better, sleep better or make love better?

185. If art is the first voice of new
human issues rising, what will be
the subjects of artists in 3000?

186. Will the next Shakespeare be an Inuit woman?

187. Which human-built structures now
in existence will still be around in
3000? What will people view as the
most beautiful building built in the
20th century?

Final Thoughts

188. What do your children think about the future? When did you last discuss it with them? How can you engage them in thinking about the future?

189. How do you feel about the future?
Are you optimistic about all the possibilities,
or pessimistic because you perceive
negative trends? Or do you feel indiffer-
ently? How would you like to feel about
the future?

190. Does looking into the future make
you feel any differently about how
you are living today?

191. When people look back at us and how we lived in 2000, what will they think about us? What will they find funny or scary? What will they envy about our lives? What will they pity?

192. When people in 3000 look back
over the millennium, what will they
wish we had learned faster?

193. What is the most positive picture you can envision for life in 3000? What can you do today to help make that vision a reality?

194. If you had to sit down and brainstorm with five people about making the future better, who would they be? What would happen if you called them now to invite them to a dinner party or brainstorming session?

About the Authors

Elizabeth Arnold has been an attorney, boiler mechanic, and CEO/founder of a general construction company. She received her JD from Harvard Law School and her BA Summa cum Laude from Yale.

Rod Beckström has been founder, CEO and Chairman of C•ATS Software Inc., a public software company acquired by Misys PLC in 1999. He is an active high-technology investor and director. He received his BA and MBA from Stanford University and was a Fulbright Scholar.

For more information on the authors, please visit our website at **www.brainticklers.com**.